THE OFF
AND AUTHORIZED
WORKBOOK FOR

THE
MOUNTAIN
IS
YOU

INTRODUCTION BY BRIANNA WIEST

CREATED BY THOUGHT CATALOG

THOUGHT
CATALOG
Books

Published by Thought Catalog Books, an imprint of Thought Catalog, a digital magazine owned and operated by The Thought & Expression Company LLC, an independent media organization founded in 2010 and based in the United States of America. For stocking inquiries, contact stockists@shopcatalog.com.

thoughtcatalog.com | shopcatalog.com

ISBN 978-1-949759-60-0

INTRODUCTION

If there's anything that I believe in, it's the strength of the human spirit. No matter how lost we may feel in life, our true selves are evergreen, and waiting for us to gain self-realization. I believe that many of the most self-destructive habits we develop are more coping mechanisms than anything else, ways to ensure that we feel safeguarded from an incredibly uncertain world. Within this knowing, we can give ourselves compassion, and then we can give ourselves grace. Once we have stopped bullying ourselves over why we cannot seem to get through the wall we're running into, we can strategize ways to get those unconscious needs met, and move forward with the lives we were meant to live. In this companion workbook to *The Mountain Is You,* I hope that you find even more support in unearthing the hidden parts of you. I hope that you feel encouraged to nurture yourself in the most fundamental ways, to envision a life beyond what you currently believe to be possible, and step forward with courage into your next era.

Brianna Wiest
August 2022

HOW TO MAKE THE MOST OF THIS WORKBOOK

You chose to read *The Mountain Is You* (and this official workbook) because you are ready to change your life. No matter what your personal mountain may be, the prompts in this workbook will serve as touchstones during your journey through the chapters of Brianna Wiest's transformative book. This guide will be your optimal companion to help you pause, reflect, and uncover what lies before you as you scale your mountain.

The goal of this workbook is to put Wiest's lessons into practice for your specific situation. It is to help you identify your own self-sabotaging behaviors and make an action plan to dismantle them.

The Official and Authorized Workbook for The Mountain Is You is a companion piece to Wiest's bestselling book. We recommend reading *The Mountain Is You* in tandem with completing this workbook. This will help you digest the information at a deeper level and apply it to your own life.

Each chapter of this workbook coincides with a chapter in *The Mountain Is You* and will provide a summary of the book's chapter and its main themes. In addition, every portion of this workbook will have an interactive section complete with reflection questions on the lessons discussed in that particular chapter.

In order to make the most of *The Official and Authorized Workbook for The Mountain Is You,* you are going to need to lean into the discomfort of the unraveling. You are going to need to be honest with yourself about your own bullshit in order to get out of your own way. You are going to need to dig deep. You are going to need to change your life and allow that blossoming to begin.

And now, we begin…

CHAPTER 1

THE MOUNTAIN IS YOU

"Your new life is going to cost you your old one."

In Chapter 1, Wiest explains what self-sabotage is and is not. As it turns out, self-sabotage is not the masochistic device you may think it is. Rather, self-sabotage is a maladaptive way of getting your (usually unconscious) needs to be met. People often self-sabotage because they do not believe they are capable of handling those needs. An example Wiest gives is sabotaging healing journeys. She writes, "Sometimes, we sabotage our healing journey by psychoanalyzing our feelings, because doing so ensures we avoid actually experiencing them."

Chapter 1 also discusses other causes of self-sabotage such as having faulty belief systems, seeking comfort over growth, and avoiding fear. Wiest shares that in order to stop self-sabotage, you need to identify why you're behaving in such a way in the first place.

CHAPTER 1 MAIN THEMES:

- Self-sabotage is a coping mechanism to get (usually unconscious) needs to be met.

- Self-sabotage is the result of an irrational fear or negative associations.

- Self-sabotage keeps us comfortable (but *also* keeps us stuck).

- Self-sabotage is guided by belief systems.

- In order to stop self-sabotaging, you must identify the root.

- Denying we have a problem does not make it go away.

- Radical change will sometimes happen when you get out of your own way, which is why many people avoid doing the healing in the first place (change is scary because it is unfamiliar).

CHAPTER 1 REFLECTION QUESTIONS

What definition of self-sabotage resonates with you the most? For example, do you use self-sabotage as a coping mechanism? Is there a specific fear holding you back from true growth? Do you have a belief system in place that keeps you stuck? Maybe a combination of all of the above? Explain which cause clicked with you most and why below:

List your three top self-sabotaging behaviors on the accompanying lines below. For example: spending time with the wrong people, overloading your schedule, overspending money, etc. :

1.

2.

3.

Finally, discuss some roadblocks you may encounter in attempting to pivot from each self-sabotaging behavior (i.e. denial, fear of change, discomfort, etc). Be as specific as possible. For example, *"I am afraid if I change, people will leave and my life will be worse than it is now."*

1.

2.

3.

What are some belief systems you subscribe to that dictate your self-sabotage? For example, if you struggle with overspending, what are your belief systems surrounding money? Or if you have trouble with forming healthy relationships, what is your current belief system pertaining to intimacy and/or vulnerability and connection?

Reflect below:

Now that you've identified your belief systems, challenge them. Explain why they don't serve you, why they could be incorrect, and what mindset would serve you better instead. For example, *"I over-spend because I live with a scarcity mindset because there was never enough money growing up, so I want to spend it while I have it. To challenge this, I need to remember I have grown up and have more opportunities than I did as a child."*

Wiest writes, "Your new life is going to cost you your old one." If you make the changes necessary to stop self-sabotaging, how will your life change? Does this excite you? Scare you? Maybe both? *Reflect on the idea of your life changing as a result of your healing in the spaces below:*

CHAPTER 2

THERE'S NO SUCH THING AS SELF-SABOTAGE

"Overcoming self-sabotage is not about trying to figure out how to override your impulses; it is first determining why those impulses exist in the first place."

Chapter 2 further builds on the premise of chapter 1, stating that self-sabotage is more self-serving than you initially may have thought. And because self-sabotage is a means of getting a desire or need to be met, you must uncover what those needs are in order to stop the behavior. As Wiest writes, "All the ways in which you are self-sabotaging are actually ways that you are feeding a need you probably do not even realize you have. Overcoming it is not only a matter of learning to understand yourself better, but realizing that your problems are not problems; they are symptoms." This means you must treat the root cause in order to eradicate the self-sabotaging behavior.

CHAPTER 2 MAIN THEMES:

- Self-sabotage is a self-serving, self-protective behavior.

- In order to stop self-sabotaging, you must determine why you're doing the things you're doing and what need is being fulfilled in doing so.

- Behaviors are symptoms, *not* the problem itself.

- There are many ways self-sabotage can present, including resistance, uprooting, hitting your upper limit, etc.

- There are various ways to determine that you may be in a self-sabotaging cycle, such as being more aware of what you *don't* want rather than what you *do* want.

- Identifying your "subconscious commitments" (i.e., feeling free, feeling safe, being loved) will help you understand and stop self-sabotage because you will know the main driving force of your behaviors and the way you lead your life.

CHAPTER 2 REFLECTION QUESTIONS

Wiest lists numerous ways self-sabotage presents itself, which are listed out below. Check mark any self-sabotaging behavior you find yourself engaging in:

- Resistance

- Hitting your upper limit

- Uprooting

- Perfectionism

- Limited emotional processing skills

- Justification

- Disorganization

- Attachment to what you don't really want

- Judging others

- Pride

- Guilt of succeeding

- Fear of failing

- Downplaying

- Unhealthy habits

- Being "busy"

- Spending time with the wrong people

- Worrying about irrational fears and least likely circumstances

Now, write out how you specifically perform each of the aforementioned self-sabotage presentations listed above on the lines below. Get as specific and detailed as possible. For example, *"I engage in 'being busy' by overloading my calendar with commitments, deadlines, and plans leaving no time for myself and my self-care."*

Based on the previous prompt, brainstorm ways to resolve the self-sabotaging behavior you discussed. Be sure to reference pages 32 through 58 in *The Mountain Is You* to do this, as these pages provide examples of how to resolve each behavior. For example, those who struggle with "being busy" can combat this self-sabotage cycle by planning out ways to streamline their schedule and make more time for themselves and their joy. They can schedule blocks of "me time" and turn their phone on do-not-disturb. Get creative and think out of the box.

Wiest describes self-sabotage behaviors as symptoms, not the actual problem. In the lines below, reflect on the potential roots of your behavioral presentations (symptoms) of self-sabotage. In other words, what need is being met by engaging in these behaviors? And how can you find a healthier way to meet this need? For example, *"I self-sabotage with busyness to feel needed and important because I've been made to feel less-than in the past. Being busy is the symptom, needing to feel valuable and important is the root. In order to feel more valuable and important, I need to look within and remind myself of my own worth. I can do this by journaling, seeing a therapist, and surrounding myself with supportive people."*

Wiest lists several signs that someone may be in a self-sabotage cycle (pages 58–62). Each of these signs are listed below with fill-in-the-blanks. Answer each question if it resonates with you.

YOU ARE MORE AWARE OF WHAT YOU DON'T WANT THAN WHAT YOU DO:

While I don't want _____

I _____ over this because I want to _____
    write verb

_____

_____

YOU'RE PUTTING YOUR HEAD IN THE SAND:

I refuse to acknowledge _____

_____ because

_____

_____

_____

YOU CARE MORE ABOUT CONVINCING OTHER PEOPLE YOU'RE OKAY THAN ACTUALLY BEING OKAY.

I pretend to be okay for everyone else because _____

_____

I don't ask for help when I need it because _____

_____

_____

YOUR MAIN PRIORITY IN LIFE IS TO BE LIKED, EVEN IF THAT COMES AS THE EXPENSE OF BEING HAPPY:

The people I seek approval from the most are _____

_____ because

_____

_____

YOU'RE MORE AFRAID OF YOUR FEELINGS THAN ANYTHING ELSE:

I am afraid to feel emotions such as _____ because

_____

_____

_____

YOU'RE BLINDLY CHASING GOALS WITHOUT ASKING YOURSELF WHY YOU WANT THOSE THINGS:

I chase goals without asking why I want those things in the first place because

_____

_____

_____

_____

_____

YOU'RE TREATING YOUR COPING
MECHANISMS AS THE PROBLEM:

I use coping mechanisms such as _____

_____

_____

_____

_____

I address these as the issue when I should really be addressing _____

_____

_____

_____

_____

YOU'RE TRYING TO CARE ABOUT EVERYTHING:

I try and care about everything because _____

_____

_____

_____

_____

_____

_____

_____

YOU ARE WAITING FOR SOMEONE ELSE TO OPEN A DOOR, OFFER APPROVAL, OR HAND YOU THE LIFE YOU HAVE BEEN WAITING FOR:

I always hold myself back and wait for someone else to give me permission

to live the life I want to live because I am _____

_____

_____

I am _____

_____

_____

because _____

_____

_____

YOU DON'T REALIZE HOW FAR YOU'VE COME:

I don't give myself enough credit for _____

_____

I will start doing so by _____

_____

_____

_____

What do you think your "subconscious commitments" are, and why? Explain below:

— CHAPTER 3 —

YOUR TRIGGERS ARE THE GUIDES TO YOUR FREEDOM

"Each 'negative' emotion we experience comes with a message, one that we do not yet know how to interpret."

Chapter 3 discusses emotions and how your feelings are actually signals and communicate when something is right or wrong for you. In the case of "negative" emotions, feelings such as anger, regret, resentment, etc., show that there is something askew and it's in your best interest to figure it out. And in understanding your emotional triggers, you understand yourself. You understand your needs, your boundaries, and your desires so you are better able to reach them.

Chapter 3 also discusses the difference between instinct and fear and explains how to tune back into your true intuition. Intuition is not a fortune teller. Rather, intuition is a response and by learning how to interpret that response, you can use it as a north star.

CHAPTER 3 MAIN THEMES:

- "Negative" emotions are signals that something is wrong, and it is up to you to figure out exactly what that something is.

- Anger, sadness, guilt, embarrassment, jealousy, resentment, regret, and chronic fear are common emotions that are actually messages for you to explore those feelings deeper.

- Wiest writes, "Within our self-sabotaging behaviors lies incredible wisdom." Self-sabotage can explain how and why we've been hurt and also what we need to do about that fact. An example Wiest gives of this includes returning over and over to a person who broke you in some sort of relationship (romantic, platonic, or otherwise). The reason you may be doing this is because these relationships feel familiar in some way, making them also feel comfortable. If this is the case, you should look back at who they remind you of and <u>why</u>.

- Part of rerouting self-sabotage is not only learning to pay attention to your internal cues but *listen* to what they are trying to communicate to you.

- Intuition is not the same as telling the future. It is a response to a given stimuli.

- "To trust your gut is not to treat it as an oracle."

- It is vital to learn how to differentiate between fear and instinct.

CHAPTER 3 REFLECTION QUESTIONS

For each section listed below, explore the "negative" emotion and what it might be trying to tell you when you experience it in your life. For example, anger may show you when a boundary was crossed.

ANGER:

SADNESS:

GUILT:

EMBARRASSMENT:

JEALOUSY:

RESENTMENT:

REGRET:

CHRONIC FEAR:

Write out validating affirmations you can turn to when you're struggling with your emotions. For example, if you're angry with a friend, you can write, "I deserve to honor my anger and communicate the boundary that was crossed." The main "negative" emotions and space for affirmations for each one are provided below.

ANGER:

SADNESS:

GUILT:

EMBARRASSMENT:

JEALOUSY:

RESENTMENT:

REGRET:

CONSTANT FEAR:

Reflect on times when your behavior was motivated by fear, *not* instincts. Write about the experience below and what you would do differently now that you are learning how to differentiate between fear and instincts:

CHAPTER 4

BUILDING EMOTIONAL INTELLIGENCE

"We are so deeply enmeshed in the mental state of 'wanting,' we cannot shift to a state of 'having.'"

In Chapter 4, Wiest gives the lowdown on emotional intelligence. "Emotional intelligence," Wiest writes, "is the ability to understand, interpret, and respond to your emotions in an enlightened and healthy way."

Wiest also discusses the neurological resistance people experience when they reach a goal. Because of the neurotransmitter dopamine, human beings always end up wanting more. This is why we often sabotage what we truly want. As Wiest says, "We know instinctively that 'arriving' won't give us the ability to abstain from life; it will only make us hungrier for more. Sometimes, we don't feel up to that challenge."

In order to combat this neurological sabotage and rise to the occasion, you need to understand why you're resisting the positive change in the first place. And then, you need to slowly become accustomed to your new life. Change happens best in microshifts, not breakthroughs.

CHAPTER 4 MAIN THEMES:

- Emotional intelligence is understanding, interpreting, and responding to emotion in a healthy way.

- Human beings are neurologically wired to resist the "good things" due to dopamine, a neurotransmitter associated with reward and pleasure that makes us crave more and more and more.

- In order to get used to a state of "having," not "wanting," you must change slowly in microshifts.

CHAPTER 4 REFLECTION QUESTIONS

Based on Wiest's definition of emotional intelligence, do you consider yourself to be emotionally intelligent? Why or why not? If not, how can you become more emotionally intelligent? Reflect and brainstorm below:

What is a large goal you're working towards (or *want* to work towards)? Why do you want it?

What has stopped you from achieving it or pursuing the aforementioned goal? Explain below.

Now that you understand what's holding you back from reaching your goals, make a plan of microshifts to work towards them below:

GOAL 1:

GOAL 2:

GOAL 3:

GOAL 4:

GOAL 5:

CHAPTER 5

RELEASING THE PAST

"Releasing the past is a process and a practice—one that we have to learn. This is where we begin."

In Chapter 5, Wiest discusses the process of letting go of the past and how it is not something you can force yourself to do. Instead, letting go involves taking the first step in a new direction. It means feeling the loss. It means building anew and rebuilding upon what you already have. Letting go means realizing that you can no longer stay where you are and where you were.

In order to let go, you must also understand the psychological processes that are involved in processing trauma and pain.

Chapter 5 also shares that you must release unrealistic expectations, such as striving for perfection. You will never be perfect, nor will your life be. Healing isn't about mending every flaw. It's about learning to exist in the space between where you are and where you want to be.

And finally, in letting go of old ideas, narratives, and beliefs that no longer serve you, you can make room for the things that do.

CHAPTER 5 MAIN THEMES:

- You cannot force yourself to let go of the past; you let go slowly and by rebuilding and building something new.

- Understanding the psychological processes behind trauma and pain will help you move forward.

- Rewriting your narrative is essential to letting go.

- "What leaves the path is clearing the path."

CHAPTER 5 REFLECTION QUESTIONS

What is something from your past that you need to release? How does it hold you back? What would happen if you finally let it go? Reflect below.

What are some unrealistic expectations you have?

Look back at an event, such as a breakup, that wounded you deeply. As you reflect on the experience, determine two things. The first, what desire was *not* reached when the painful thing happened. The second, what the root of that desire is and means to you. Reference the section "The Psychological Trick To Release Old Experiences" on page 141 to complete this exercise.

Rewrite your narrative about a painful experience.

Building off of the previous prompt, if you let go of this pain, what do you make room for? Be specific.

How can you feel safe in your own life again? Reference section "Recovering From Emotional Trauma" on page 154 to complete this exercise. Reflect on what would be needed to feel safe below:

— CHAPTER 6 —

BUILDING A NEW FUTURE

"When we release, we are wiping the slate clean to create something better."

Chapter 6 springboards off of Chapter 5, inviting us to focus on the future now that we are beginning to let go of the past. Chapter 6 reminds us that we must keep our eyes facing forward, not backward, in order to keep moving in that direction.

Chapter 6 also focuses on the concept of meeting your future self through a variety of exercises such as inner child work and imagining your future self.

CHAPTER 6 MAIN THEMES:

- Letting go of the past is the springboard to a better future.

- Picturing your highest future self helps you work towards becoming that person.

- Inner child work can be incredibly helpful in healing your adult self.

- Trauma is not just in your head; it is also in your body. Uncovering and noticing where you are tight or tense your body can help you process trauma.

- Becoming your most powerful sefl takes work, including being disliked, knowing your weaknesses, and having self-awareness.

- Validating your own feelings is vital to moving through them.

- Developing your own principles surrounding things that you struggle with such as relationships, money, work, or just life is imperative to forming a strong sense of self and purpose. It also helps create a steady foundation and give you more direction.

CHAPTER 6 REFLECTION QUESTIONS

Step 1: Face the fear first

As Wiest instructs on page 176, sit in a quiet place with a journal (or these pages!) and imagine your highest future self. Describe your initial thoughts below:

Step 2: Notice how your future self looks. How do they behave? How do they communicate?

Step 3: Ask for guidance. Ask your future self all the questions you want to be answered.

Step 4: Imagine your future self handing you the "keys" to your new life. What are those keys?

On pages 180 to 183, Wiest gives advice on how to process trauma by focusing on the physical manifestations of that trauma. Reference these pages while filling out the below prompts.

What are some ways you can bring yourself out of survival mode? For example, doing a yoga flow, trying meditation, drinking a cold glass of water, etc. List some ideas below:

Based on what your trauma was (i.e. relationships, finances, etc.), write about how you can restore a sense of safety in those areas of your life now.

Finally, write out some ways you try and predict the future. For example, "People will always hurt me in the end." Then, rewrite it. For example, "People may hurt me. And they may not. But the point is, I will be okay either way."

The next three questions will pertain to finding your principles. Reference pages 194 through 203 for these questions.

1. What are your values? List them below:

2. **What feelings do you want to experience most in life?**

3. **What makes you uneasy or gives you anxiety?**

The final questions will help you find out what you truly want to do with your life. Reference pages 203 to 205 for these questions.

Who and what is worth suffering for?

If social media wasn't a thing, how would you spend your time?

What comes most naturally to you?

What would your ideal daily routine consist of?

What do you want your legacy to be?

CHAPTER 7

FROM SELF-SABOTAGE TO SELF-MASTERY

"Your life is just beginning."

Chapter 7 pulls together everything you've learned about self-sabotage and how to transform it into self-mastery. To transform yourself from someone who self-sabotages to someone who is the master of their own destiny is to realize that you were the one holding yourself back in the first place. This means you also have the power to change and move yourself and your life forward.

Chapter 7 discusses controlling emotions vs. suppressing them, as well as how to trust yourself again, find peace, detach from worrying, become mentally strong, and truly enjoy your life.

CHAPTER 7 MAIN THEMES:

- How to control your emotions vs. suppress them.

- How to trust yourself again.

- The importance of creating aligned goals.

- Finding peace.

- Detaching from worrying.

- Remembering that feelings are not always facts.

- How to become mentally strong.

- How to truly enjoy your life.

CHAPTER 7 REFLECTION QUESTIONS

What are the emotions you suppress most? What are you trying to control in doing so? For example, *"I suppress my anger because I'm afraid someone will leave me if I express it."*

Do you trust yourself? Why or why not? If you *don't* trust yourself, how can you get to a point where you *do*?

What is your inner child afraid of? How will you comfort them?

What does peace sound like to you? Describe it. Be as specific as possible but most importantly, be authentic and honest about what it sounds like for you, *no one* else:

What is an ongoing problem in your life, and what is your plan to fix it?

List three things you need help with and name people who can help you conquer those things.

1.

Who can help me conquer this?

2.

Who can help me conquer this?

3.

Who can help me conquer this?

How will you ask for help? What will you say? Draft it below:

Challenge any ways you engage in false dichotomous thinking. For example, "If I lose my job, I am a failure. This is false because no one job will dictate my worth as a human being."

Reflect on why you don't want to feel happy all the time.

Wiest writes, "The greatest gift life will hand you is discomfort." Reflect on this below and what discomfort has brought and will bring you.

On pages 229 to 237, Wiest lists ways to be happy. Which suggestions resonate with you the most? Why? And how will you implement these into your life?

Who will you become climbing your own mountain? What did the mountain teach you? What will the mountain teach you? Write it out below:

THOUGHT CATALOG Books

Thought Catalog Books is a publishing imprint of Thought Catalog, a digital magazine for thoughtful storytelling, and is owned and operated by The Thought & Expression Company, an independent media group based in the United States of America. Founded in 2010, we are committed to helping people become better communicators and listeners to engender a more exciting, attentive, and imaginative world. The Thought Catalog Books imprint connects Thought Catalog's digital-native roots with our love of traditional book publishing. The books we publish are designed as beloved art pieces. We publish work we love. Pioneering an author-first and holistic approach to book publishing, Thought Catalog Books has created numerous best-selling print books, audiobooks, and eBooks that are being translated in over 30 languages, including Brianna Wiest's bestselling book, *The Mountain Is You.*

ThoughtCatalog.com | **Thoughtful Storytelling**

ShopCatalog.com | **Shop Books + Curated Products**

MORE FROM
THOUGHT CATALOG BOOKS
AND BRIANNA WIEST

The Mountain Is You

*101 Essays That Will Change
The Way You Think*

*When You're Ready,
This Is How You Heal*

Ceremony

I Am The Hero Of My Own Life

Salt Water